Grandmothers: God's Gift to Children

By Mary Blount Christian
Illustrated by Susan Morris

"A good man [woman]
leaves an inheritance to his [her]
children's children."
Proverbs 13:22

CONCORDIA®
Publishing House
St. Louis

Copyright © 1982
Concordia Publishing House
3558 South Jefferson Avenue
Saint Louis, Missouri 63118

Manufactured in the United States of America

Library of Congress Cataloging in Publication Data

Christian, Mary Blount.
    Grandmothers, God's gift to children.

    Summary: A girl and her grandmother work out ways to practice
Jesus's work.
    1. Children—Religious life. 2. Grandmothers—Juvenile literature.
[1. Christian life. 2. Grandmothers] I. Title.
BV4571.2.C46   248.8'2   81-22225
ISBN 0-570-04068-X   AACR2

1 2 3 4 5 6 7 8 9 10   SB   91 90 89 88 87 86 87 84 83 82

Remembering
Mammy Dill
and
Grandma Blount

THE TOWER

A girl sits on the floor
of Harlequin linoleum,
stacking alphabet blocks
one on top of the other.
"Look at my house, Gamma,"
she says.
"I'm building it to heaven."

The woman puts down
her paintbrush and wipes her hands
on the spattered rag that hangs
on her easel.

Suddenly the blocks clatter and tumble,
scattering under chairs
and against the walls.

"Oh, Gamma, my sky house fell,"
the girl wails.

The woman stoops to retrieve
a block from beneath her easel.
"People once tried to build
a tower to heaven," she says.

The girl picks a block
from under the chair.
"I remember—the Tower of Babel,"
the girl replies.
"That one didn't work either."

The woman hands the block
to the girl and smiles.
She sits on the floor
opposite the girl.
"Why don't we build
a bridge to each other instead?"
she asks.

5

THE SPECIAL GIFT

A woman kneels at her closet.
She searches through the scraps
of cloth and old clothes.
"What are you doing, Grandmaw?"
a girl asks.

"Tomorrow a truck comes,"
the woman replies.
"It will collect old things
to be resold.
The money helps buy food
for people in need.
I'm looking for nice old things."

"Why would anyone buy old things?"
the girl asks her grandmother.
"I like nice NEW Things."

The woman measures a length
of white cloth.
"This is enough for a blouse,"
she says.
She puts it in the basket.

"New things are nice," she agrees.
"But some people cannot buy
new things as easily as old.
And I cannot give new things.
Still I want to share what I have."

The girl runs her fingers over
the smooth, white material.
"Like the widow's mite?"
she asks the woman.

The woman's face brightens.
"Yes," she says, "the widow's mite.
"It pleases Jesus
when we share what we have."

The girl leaves, but soon returns.
She clutches a doll
with tousled hair
and a stuffed bear
with a rip in its paw.

"What about these?" she asks.

The woman studies the items.
"I'm sure we can repair them
as good as new," she replies.
"How pleased Jesus must be
with my little granddaughter!"

NEW LOVE

A woman cradles a baby
in her arms and hums.
A boy stands at her knee, watching.
"She belongs to us, Grandy?"
the boy asks. "She is ours?"

The woman shifts the baby
to one side and pulls the boy
into her lap, too.
"She will soon belong,"
the woman replies—
"when the adoption papers
are all signed."

"Why did her mommy give her away?"
the child asks.
"Didn't she love her?"

"Giving her away doesn't mean
she didn't love her,"
Grandy replies.
"Remember the story
of Baby Moses in the Bible?"

The boy's eyes sparkle
as he recalls.
He places his finger close
to the baby's hand.
She clutches his finger tightly.

"Moses' mother gave him away
BECAUSE she loved him so much.
I want to think the same
is true for OUR baby, don't you?"
Grandy asks.

The boy kisses his grandmother
on the cheek.
"Yes, that is what
I think, too," he says.

9

THE LOST ONE

A boy darts frantically
through the department store.
He passes dozens of faces,
all of them strangers.
He pushes through rows of counters,
past streams of legs
and bulky packages.

Suddenly he sees a woman.
Her look of panic
matches his own.

They rush into each other's arms,
hugging and kissing.
"Oh, thank God!" the woman says.

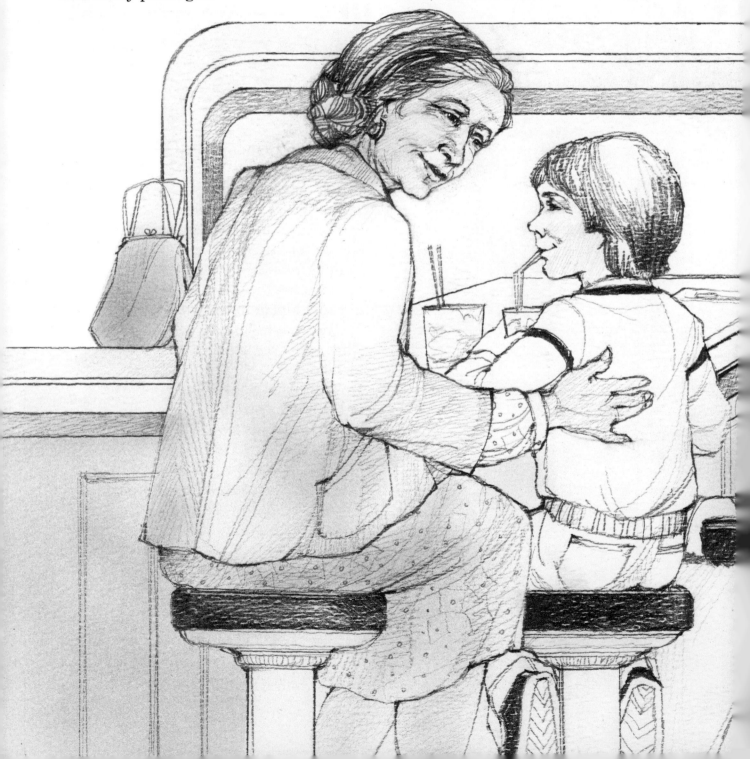

"I was so scared when I saw
you weren't with me."

"You, Granny?' the boy asks.
"You were scared, too?"

She holds his hand tightly.
Together they step into

the store's restaurant.
They order lemonade before
either says another word.

"Of course I was scared,"
the woman admits.
"Now I know just how Mary
must have felt when Jesus
was not in their caravan."

"I remember the story!"
the boy exclaims.
"Mary thought he was with Joseph.
And Joseph thought he was with Mary.
But Jesus was really at the temple."

The woman nods.
"How frightening it must have been!"
she says.

The boy squeezes her hand.
"I'm glad we found each other,"
he says.

THE OLD ONE

A girl rushes into the kitchen,
a blossom clutched tightly
in her small hand.
Carefully she places it
in the bud vase already
on the tray.

"Grandy will like my flower,"
the girl says, watching
as her mother places the plate
of food on the tray.

She follows her mother
up the stairs, their feet
clicking against each step.

Together they enter
a room the color of sunshine
where an old woman sits,
stroking a caramel cat.

Curiously the girl touches
the woman's dry, wrinkled face.
She touches her own,
as if comparing them.

"Will I be old someday, too, Grandy?"
the girl asks curiously.

The old woman chuckles.
"Oh, child, we all get there
someday, of course.
But you have a long time to go.
Remember, I'm your GREAT
grandmother."

The girl nods.
"Daddy's momma's momma,"
she recalls.
"Did Isaac think Sarah was old?"
she asks.

The old woman sniffs the blossom.
"Why, I suppose he did,"
she replies.
"But Sarah was even older than I
when Isaac was born."

"She was the oldest momma
there ever ever was,"
the girl says.

The old woman pats the girl's cheek.
"That's the best proof I know of
that God rewards faith," she says.

The girl scrambles to the window sill
to stroke the caramel cat
while the old woman eats.

The cat stretches and yawns,
then leaps to the window sill.
"Grandy!" the girl calls,
scrambling into the old woman's lap.

The woman reaches her thin arms
around the child to hug her.
Outside the window
bees buzz around a coral vine.

13

THE JUDGE

A girl wiggles on a bench
that smells of lemon oil.
CLUNK! The gavel sounds
as the woman at the high desk
strikes it once, twice.
"Court is dismissed,"
the woman says.

The girl scoots
through the small wooden gate
and up to the high desk.
The woman in the dark robe
smiles and scoops the girl
into her arms.

14

Inside the woman drapes
her robe around the girl.
It touches the floor,
dragging behind her.

"Are you the only lady judge?"
the girl asks her grandmother.
"No," the woman replies.
"There are many women who are judges.
There was even a woman judge
in the Bible—remember Deborah?"

The girl hands the robe
back to the woman.
She climbs into the leather desk chair
and spins dizzily.

"I remember," the girl says at last.
"She sat under the Deborah Tree."

"Yes," her grandmother says.
"And people came
to ask her questions."

"I think I would like it better,"
the girl says thoughtfully,
"if you had a Grandmother Tree
instead of that big quiet room."

The woman laughs and stops
the spinning chair long enough to give
the girl a big hug.

"I liked watching you,
Grandma," the girl says.
"But it is hard to be still
and quiet for so long."

The woman laughs.
"Come inside my chambers,"
she tells the girl,
"and you can be as noisy
and wiggly as you want."

THE HARP

A woman's fingers skim over
the strings of a harp,
and music fills the hall.

A boy closes his eyes and nods
in time to the music.
"You play pretty, Mimi,"
he tells the woman.
"I wish I could play, too."

The woman pulls him closer
and guides his small hands
across the strings.

"My music is not so pretty
as yours," he tells the woman.

"It takes years of practicing,"
she tells him, smiling.
"I didn't play like this
in the beginning."

The boy giggles.
"You should have been a shepherd,
like David," he says.
"David could practice his harp
in the hills where no one
heard his mistakes."

The woman laughs.
"Here,' she says, replacing
his hands on the strings.
"Let's see if you can make music
fit for a king, too."

BEING BRAVE

The chambers of the city council
are hushed as a woman finishes
her speech.
Then everyone claps.
The woman nods and takes her seat
next to a young woman and a girl.

"I am so PROUD of you, Mother,"
the younger woman says.
"That took a lot of courage."

The girl moves closer.
"Gramma, you didn't even shake.
You weren't scared at all.
You are as brave as Queen Esther!"

The woman looks around
the crowded room.
She hugs the girl to her.
"Oh, I was scared all right.
And I think Queen Esther
was scared, too."

"But she did such a brave thing!"
the girl argues.

"It isn't doing the things
we aren't scared of
that makes us brave,"
the woman says.
"It is doing things
even when we ARE scared
that makes us brave."

"Like when I answer a question
in school?" the girl asks.
"Even when I'm all shaky inside?"

"Yes," the woman answers,
squeezing her hand.
"Even when you are shaky inside."

THE HEN

A windmill spins dizzily
in the same hot breeze that brings
the sweet scent of clover to them.
The soft dust lifts and stirs
to settle once more at their feet.

The boy follows closely behind
the woman, watching anxiously.
Dozens of chickens clamor
around them.

The woman reaches into the folds
of her checked apron
and scatters corn on the ground.
The chickens squawk and cluck
and peck eagerly
at the yellow kernels.

The boy dips into the apron folds
and scatters a small handful
of grain, too.
He giggles as the chickens
quickly gobble it up.

"Look, Gran," the boy shouts.
He points to a hen
with a dozen downy chicks
scrambling to keep up with her.

"Why do the little chicks stay
so close to their mother, Gran?"
he asks, puzzled.

"She protects them,
just as Jesus protects us," Gran says.
"Jesus once compared Himself
to a hen gathering her chicks
under her wings."

Smiling, the boy throws
a handful of grain
near the hen and her chicks.

Slowly the chicks venture out
under the protective eye
of the mother hen
to share the grain.

21

THE TRAVELERS

A woman and a boy drive
along the pasture-lined highway.
The sun bounces from the concrete,
making the land seem to undulate
before their eyes.

They pass an empty car
at the side of the road.
One tire is flat.
In a while they see
a young woman walking.
She carries a small child.
Another stumbles along,
clinging to her pants leg.
They look hot and tired.

"I think that is their car
with the flat,' the boy says.

"I think you are right,"
the woman agrees.
She pulls her truck to the side.
"I will take you to a garage,"
the woman offers.
"You and your children climb in."

The five of them
bounce along the highway.
Soon they come to a garage.
The young woman helps
her children from the truck.
She thanks the woman for the ride.

The woman and the boy wave good-bye,
then turn back to go home.

"You are just like the good Samaritan,"
the boy tells his grandmother.

The woman smiles at her grandson.
"Sometimes it is easy
to be a good Samaritan.
Sometimes it is not."